SUPERMAN

ANNUAL 2014

TITAN COMICS

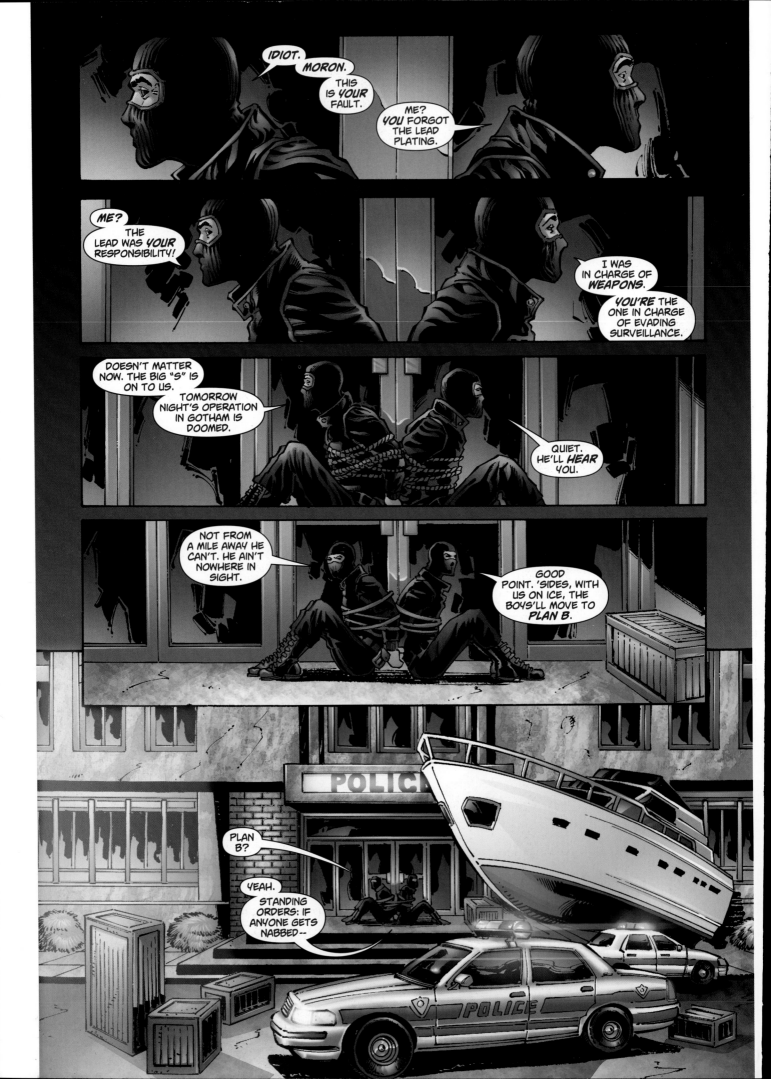

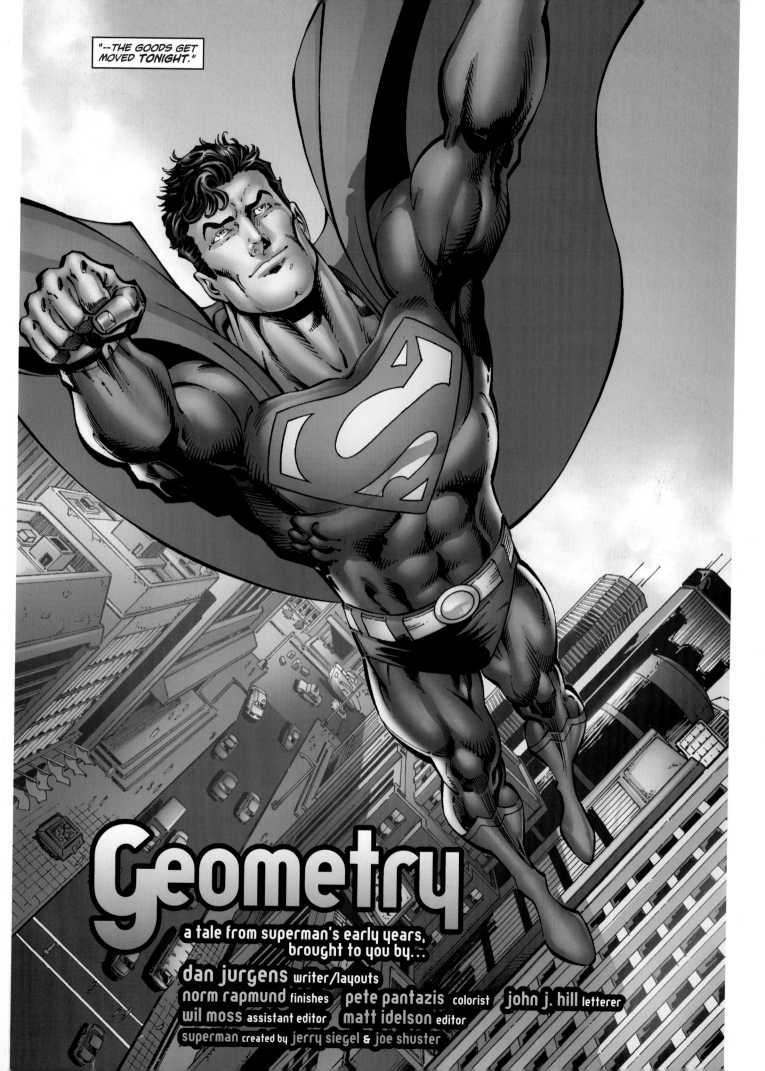

YOU KNOW THE SAYING, "NO ONE KNOWS WHAT GOES ON BEHIND CLOSED DOORS"? WAYNE MANOR IS LIVING PROOF OF THAT.

NO CAPE TONIGHT?

NO MASK?

YOU'RE JUST DOING THE *BRUCE WAYNE* BIT?

WOW. I DIDN'T THINK THAT WAS *POSSIBLE.*

MUCH TO MASTER BRUCE'S DISMAY, I'M SURE, RICHARD.

THERE ARE A FEW OCCASIONS PER YEAR WHEN WAYNE ENTERPRISES DEMANDS MY ATTENDANCE.

LUCIUS TELLS ME THIS IS ONE OF THEM.

THE GUY IN THE TUX IS BRUCE WAYNE. NICE ENOUGH TO TAKE IN AN ORPHAN LIKE ME, BUT NOT EXACTLY MR. HUMOROUS.

THE STOCKHOLDERS MUST SEE YOU PERIODICALLY, SIR.

GOTHAM CITY WILL HAVE TO SURVIVE WITHOUT BATMAN FOR ONE NIGHT.

WHAT ABOUT *ME*?

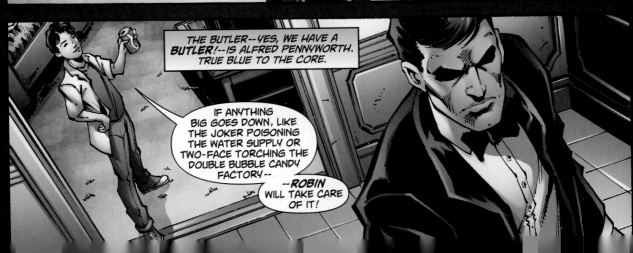

THE BUTLER--YES, WE HAVE A *BUTLER!*--IS ALFRED PENNYWORTH. TRUE BLUE TO THE CORE.

IF ANYTHING BIG GOES DOWN, LIKE THE JOKER POISONING THE WATER SUPPLY OR TWO-FACE TORCHING THE DOUBLE BUBBLE CANDY FACTORY--

--*ROBIN* WILL TAKE CARE OF IT!

"COMPLICATIONS"?

I'M THEIR COMPLICATION.

GOTTA BE QUICK.

SILENT.

WHO NEEDS BATMAN?

A COUPLE A' GIRL SCOUTS COULD HANDLE THESE GUYS.

THEY GOT NUTHIN'.

ABSOLUTELY--

--NUTHIN'?

C'MERE, BRAT.

OH.

LOOKS LIKE WE GOT US A DO-GOODER, MAX.

SO WE DO. GET THE ANCHOR FROM THE BOAT. TIME FOR THIS BIRD TO BE A FISH.

WEIRD. THE HIGH AND MIGHTY BAT SENT A KID TO DO HIS WORK FOR HIM.

AT LEAST THIS AIN'T LIKE METROPOLIS, WHERE WE GOTTA WORRY ABOUT THE BIG "S."

WHY DON'T WE JUST SHOOT HIM AND BE DONE WITH IT?

IF THE BAT'S NEARBY, I DON'T WANT HIM HEARIN' THE SHOTS. DO IT.

SROOSH

I NEED A RESET BUTTON.

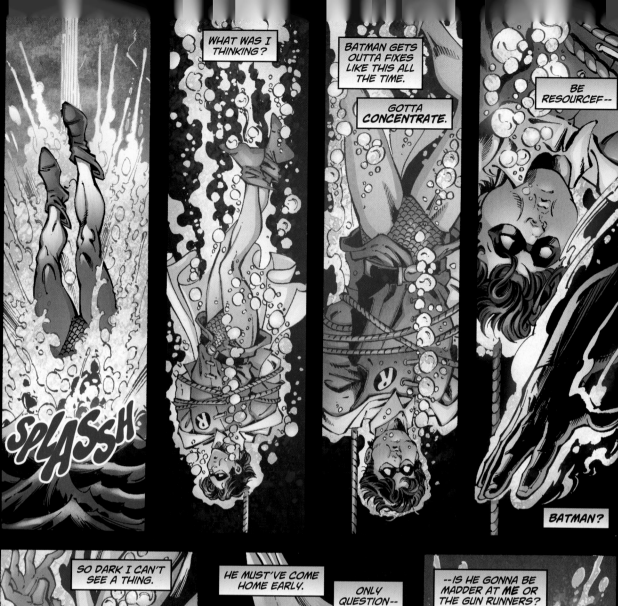

SPLASSH

WHAT WAS I THINKING?

BATMAN GETS OUTTA FIXES LIKE THIS ALL THE TIME.

GOTTA CONCENTRATE.

BE RESOURCEF--

BATMAN?

SO DARK I CAN'T SEE A THING.

BUT I'M FREE.

HE MUST'VE COME HOME EARLY.

ONLY QUESTION--

--IS HE GONNA BE MADDER AT ME OR THE GUN RUNNERS?

WAIT. YOU?!

YOU'RE... HERE.

WHA... WHAT'S UP? IS THE JOKER ON THE LOOSE?

YOU WERE HERE ALL NIGHT?

WITH ALL THE HOMEWORK I HADDA DO, YEAH. WHERE ELSE WOULD I BE?

THOUGHT YOU MIGHT HAVE GONE AFTER THE SMUGGLERS.

BUT IF YOU WERE HERE ALL NIGHT--

--THEN THAT MEANS--

--YOUR GEOMETRY ASSIGNMENT--

--IS--

--DONE?

OF... COURSE IT'S DONE. TOTALLY DONE!

NICE WORK, DICK. GO BACK TO SLEEP.

THANK YOU, SUPERMAN!

"G'MORNIN', MR. KENT!"

I MET A GUY DOWNSTAIRS WHO LEFT A NOTE FOR YOU. IT'S ON YOUR DESK.

THANK YOU, JIMMY.

Next time, make sure the boy does his own homework so he actually learns something. And don't leave the cycle at the scene.

WHATEVER YOU SAY, BRUCE. WHATEVER YOU SAY.

END

SECRETS OF THE

JOR-EL AND LARA.
Thirty-foot statues created by Superman in honor of his birth parents watch over the entrance to various living quarters.

2

SUNSTONE SIMULATOR.
Created out of the sunstone memory crystals sent with Superman to Earth, this databank holds the historical and scientific knowledge of Krypton. Hosted by a simulation of his father, Jor-El, this extra-terrestrial computer is Superman's most valuable and cherished heirloom.

1

INTERPLANETARY HABITAT.
Across the universe, Superman has rescued an array of extraterrestrial animals on the verge of extinction including the Thought-Beast, the Duplorian Hawk, the Metal Boar and the Black Mercy.

3

FORTRESS OF SOLITUDE

THE PHANTOM ZONE PORTAL.
A view screen able to peer into various depths of the phantom zone.

6

THE BOTTLE CITY OF KANDOR.
Named after the fabled Kryptonian city of Kandor, this diverse metropolis of extra-terrestrial races was shrunken down utilizing Coluan science and kept by the wizard Tolos until Superman rescued it.

4

THE PHANTOM ZONE PROJECTOR.
After discovering an extradimensional void, Jor-El fought against the council's death penalty laws and developed the phantom zone projector.

5

TROPHY ROOM AND MUSEUM.
Superman's private collection of relics from his adventures and statues of his family, friends and enemies from the past, present and future.

8

THE KEY.
A landmark from the original Fortress of Solitude, this once unlocked its giant doors.

7

SUPER-SCIENCE LAB.
Within these walls Superman performs secret and mysterious experiments in an attempt to cure Mon-El's lead-poisoning, enlarge the city of Kandor and negate his own vulnerability to kryptonite.

9

THE ATOMIC CAULDRON.
The most powerful furnace in the world fuels the Fortress of Solitude. Due to the high temperatures, the liquefied sunstone crystal core is operated and cared for by Superman Robots.

10

SUPER-WEAPONS ROOM.
This room contains the confiscated weapons of Superman's enemies. Within this heavily guarded area, Superman studies them, hoping to find something of societal value in their technology.

11

SUPERMAN'S WARSUIT.
Originally a prototype designed by Lex Luthor to combat Superman, this warsuit was rebuilt by the Man of Steel to protect him from the very kryptonite weapons it once contained.

12

SUPERMAN'S TOP 10 MOST WANTED!

LEX LUTHOR--A BRILLIANT MIND CORRUPTED BY HIS OWN INSATIABLE EGO, LEX LUTHOR IS OBSESSED WITH THE DEFAMATION AND DESTRUCTION OF THE ONE MAN HE CAN NEVER OVERSHADOW--SUPERMAN. HIS CURRENT WHEREABOUTS ARE UNKNOWN, ALTHOUGH HE HAS TAKEN RESPONSIBILITY FOR RECENT ABNORMAL SUNSPOT ACTIVITY.

BRAINIAC--BRAINIAC IS FROM THE PLANET COLU. HIS "TWELFTH-LEVEL INTELLIGENCE" MAKES HIM THE SMARTEST BEING IN THE ENTIRE UNIVERSE. HE IS ALSO THE COLDEST. FROM SHRINKING CITIES TO ANNIHILATING ENTIRE ALIEN RACES, BRAINIAC VIEWS THE UNIVERSE AS HIS OWN PERSONAL LAB AND WILL COMMIT ANY ACT IN THE NAME OF SCIENCE. HE IS ESPECIALLY FASCINATED WITH SUPERMAN AND HIS WEALTH OF KRYPTONIAN KNOWLEDGE.

GENERAL ZOD--FORMER LEADER OF THE PLANET KRYPTON'S MILITARY, ZOD WAS SENTENCED TO THE PHANTOM ZONE FOR HERESY, MURDER AND TREASON AFTER AN ATTEMPTED COUP AGAINST THE KRYPTONIAN COUNCIL. GENERAL ZOD HAS ONE AMBITION--TO RULE THE PLANET EARTH AFTER THE DEATH OF HIS JAILER'S SON.

URSA--FORMER LIEUTENANT OF THE PLANET KRYPTON'S MILITARY, URSA WAS SENTENCED TO THE PHANTOM ZONE FOR HERESY, MURDER AND TREASON. HER HATRED OF ALL MANKIND THREATENS EVEN THE CHILDREN AROUND HER.

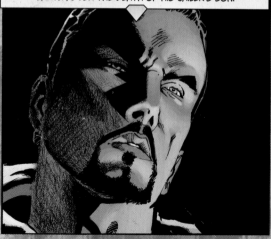

NON--ONCE A MEMBER OF THE COUNCIL AND FRIEND TO JOR-EL, NON'S FALL FROM GRACE AND CURRENT CONDITION REMAINS A MYSTERY. DRAFTED INTO GENERAL ZOD'S WAR, NON WAS SENTENCED TO THE PHANTOM ZONE FOR HERESY, MURDER AND TREASON. UNABLE TO SPEAK AND BARELY ABLE TO THINK, NON HAS BECOME A FORCE OF PURE RAGE AND DESTRUCTION.

BIZARRO--THE IMPERFECT CLONE OF SUPERMAN, BIZARRO IS THE OPPOSITE OF THE MAN OF STEEL IN EVERY WAY. HIS HEART IS ON HIS LEFT SIDE, HIS SYNAPSES MISFIRE EVERY TIME A THOUGHT GOES THROUGH HIS HEAD AND HE SHEDS HIS CHALKY SKIN LIKE A SNAKE. REPROGRAMMED BY LEX LUTHOR, BIZARRO HAS GAINED A HIGHER LEVEL OF MENTAL CONTROL THAN HE HAS PREVIOUSLY DISPLAYED, COMPARABLE TO THAT OF A FOUR-YEAR OLD BOY.

PARASITE--RUDY JONES WAS A LEECH ON EVERYONE IN HIS LIFE FOR YEARS BEFORE HE WAS EXPOSED TO RADIOACTIVE WASTE AND TRANSFORMED INTO THE ENERGY-SUCKING PARASITE. TRAPPED IN A CONSTANT STATE OF HUNGER, THE POWER HE DRAINS FROM SUPERMAN IS THE ONLY ONE STRONG ENOUGH TO TRULY SATISFY HIM.

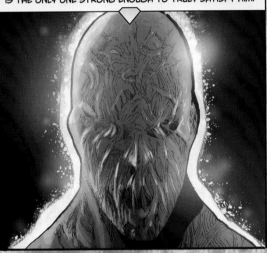

MR. MXYZPTLK-- MR. MXYZPTLK (MIX-YEZ-PITTLE-IK) IS AN IMP FROM THE FIFTH DIMENSION. ENTERTAINED BY THE ADVENTURES OF SUPERMAN, MXYZPTLK IS ABLE TO TRAVEL TO EARTH EVERY 90 DAYS UPON WHICH HE USES HIS NEARLY LIMITLESS POWER TO POSE TESTS AND CHALLENGES FOR THE MAN OF STEEL. HE WAS LAST SEEN 190 DAYS AGO. WHY HE HASN'T SHOWN HIMSELF YET IS UNKNOWN.

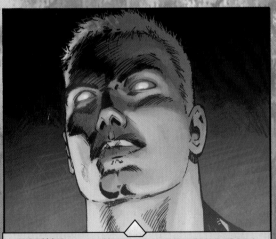

METALLO: JOHN CORBEN WAS A THIEF PULLED FROM A NEAR FATAL CAR CRASH AND TRANSFORMED INTO A CYBERNETIC MONSTER POWERED BY A HEART OF GREEN KRYPTONITE. CORBEN WAS RENAMED METALLO AFTER THE ALLOY LACED WITHIN HIS SKELETON. RECENTLY, METALLO HAS BEEN SEARCHING FOR A WAY TO ENHANCE HIS POWER LEVELS.

TOYMAN: A BRILLIANT TOYMAKER, WINSLOW SCHOTT WAS DEEMED OBSOLETE BY THE TOY COMPANY HE HELPED BUILD AND FIRED. SCHOTT TURNS HIS SKILLS AGAINST SOCIETY, TRANSFORMING HIS TOYS INTO LETHAL KILLING MACHINES TARGETING ADULTS. SCHOTT WAS LATER IMPRISONED IN ARKHAM ASYLUM FOR KILLING A CHILD. THE TRUTH BEHIND THIS HEINOUS ACT IS STILL UNCLEAR.

31

33

34

35

YOU MUST BE MR. KENT. I'M SALLY KENNARD.

PLEASE, CALL ME *CLARK.*

CLASS, THIS IS MR. CLARK KENT FROM THE DAILY PLANET. HE'S DONE A LOT OF COVERAGE ON *SUPERMAN* AND HE'S HERE TODAY TO COVER OUR SUPERMAN *APPRECIATION DAY* FOR HIS NEWSPAPER.

PLEASE, DON'T LET ME *INTERRUPT...*

WELL, WE WERE ACTUALLY JUST DISCUSSING WHAT IT IS THAT WE THINK SUPERHEROES LIKE SUPERMAN *DO.*

OH, THAT'S EASY. THEY *HELP* PEOPLE, RIGHT?

WELL, I'M AFRAID THAT MOST OF MY STUDENTS IN THIS ROOM SEEM TO THINK THEY MOSTLY *HIT* PEOPLE.

HIT PEOPLE!? WHAT'S HEROIC ABOUT *THAT?*

MARGARET?

BECAUSE SOMETIMES THERE'S A *BAD GUY?* Um, AND HE'S *HURTING* PEOPLE?

Um, AND SO THE HERO HAS TO COME AND MAKE HIM *STOP* WHICH MAYBE MEANS *BEATING* HIM UP.

Hm. I SEE WHAT YOU'RE SAYING, BUT I WONDER...

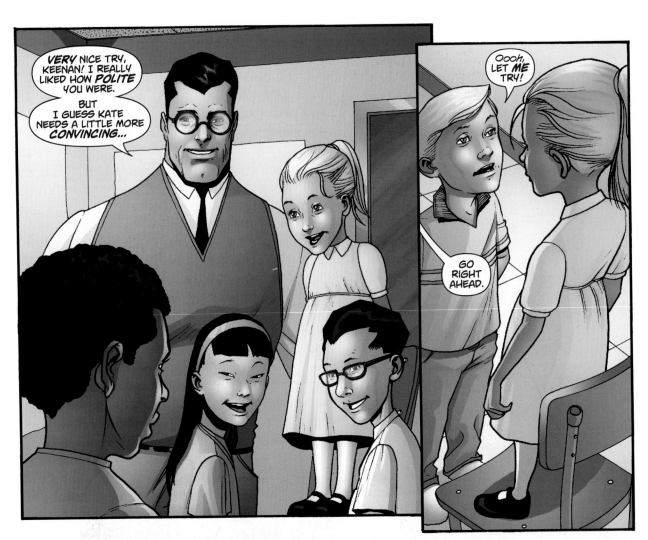

VERY NICE TRY, KEENAN! I REALLY LIKED HOW *POLITE* YOU WERE.

BUT I GUESS KATE NEEDS A LITTLE MORE *CONVINCING...*

Oooh, LET *ME* TRY!

GO RIGHT AHEAD.

KATE, IF YOU LET MR. KENT GO AND STOP STEPPING ALL OVER METROPOLIS, I'LL LET YOU USE MY SECRET *SCRIBBLERITE* PEN!

IT WRITES *INVISIBLE* AND YOU CAN ONLY READ IT IF YOU PUT *LEMON JUICE* ON IT SO YOU CAN USE IT FOR SECRET *MESSAGES* AND STUFF.

BRIBERY. INTERESTING.

WHAT DO YOU *THINK,* KATE? ARE YOU GOING TO GO FOR THAT?

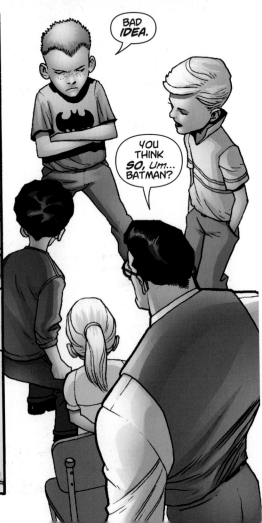

BAD IDEA.

YOU THINK *SO,* UM... BATMAN?

EVEN IF SHE TAKES THE PEN, IT'LL DRY *UP* SOON, AND THEN SHE'LL BE EVEN *MADDER* THAN SHE IS NOW AND SHE'LL TAKE, LIKE, EVEN *MORE* HOSTAGES.

OH, AND I SUPPOSE *YOU'VE* GOT A *BETTER* IDEA?

WELL, *DUH.*

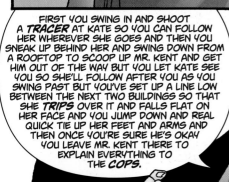

FIRST YOU SWING IN AND SHOOT A *TRACER* AT KATE SO YOU CAN FOLLOW HER WHEREVER SHE GOES AND THEN YOU SNEAK UP BEHIND HER AND SWING DOWN FROM A ROOFTOP TO SCOOP UP MR. KENT AND GET HIM OUT OF THE WAY BUT YOU LET KATE SEE YOU SO SHE'LL FOLLOW AFTER YOU AS YOU SWING PAST BUT YOU'VE SET UP A LINE LOW BETWEEN THE NEXT TWO BUILDINGS SO THAT SHE *TRIPS* OVER IT AND FALLS FLAT ON HER FACE AND YOU JUMP DOWN AND REAL QUICK TIE UP HER FEET AND ARMS AND THEN ONCE YOU'RE SURE HE'S OKAY YOU LEAVE MR. KENT THERE TO EXPLAIN EVERYTHING TO THE *COPS.*

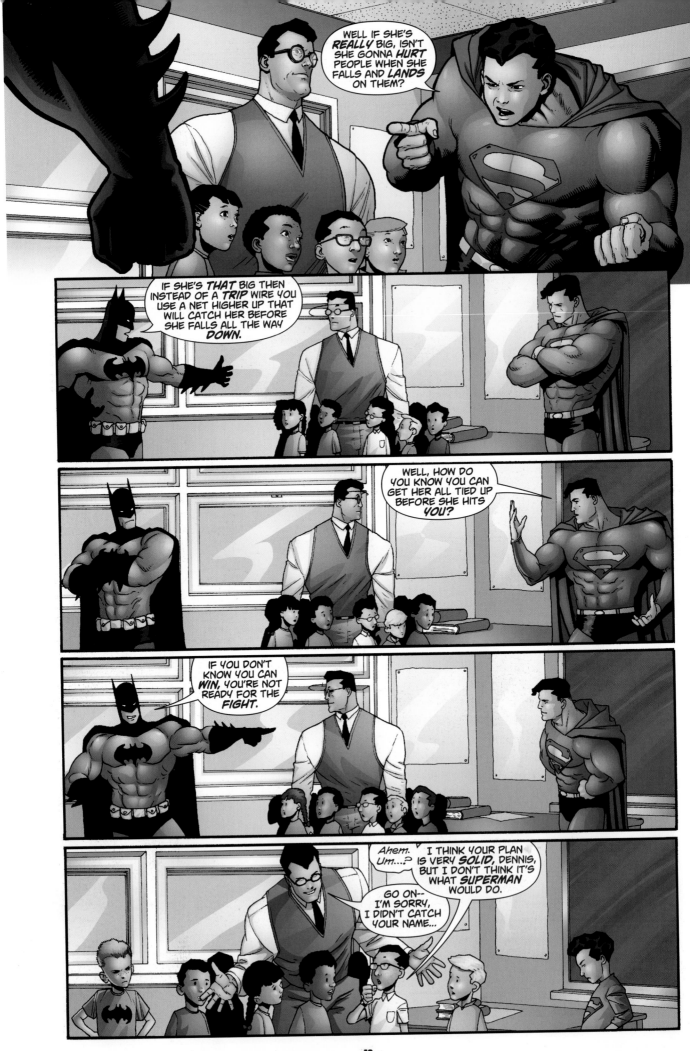

42

WHEN SUPERMAN FIRST CAME HERE HE ONLY HAD THE SPACESHIP HE *CRASHED* IN.

WHEN HE DISCOVERED THAT HE WAS VERY STRONG AND COULD FLY AND COULD NOT BE HURT BY MOST THINGS, SUPERMAN WANTED TO *HELP* PEOPLE.

SUPERMAN IS NOT ACTUALLY MADE OUT OF STEEL. PEOPLE JUST SAY THAT BECAUSE OF HOW STRONG HE IS.

IF HE WERE STILL ON HIS HOME PLANET HE THINKS THAT PROBABLY HE WOULD BE JUST LIKE EVERYONE ELSE THERE.

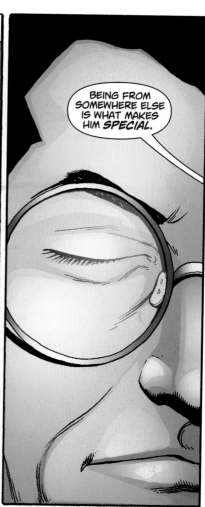

BEING FROM SOMEWHERE ELSE IS WHAT MAKES HIM *SPECIAL.*

THAT WAS VERY NICE, ARMANJANI, THANK YOU.

KATE?

CAN I GO NEXT!?

MAY YOU GO NEXT, AND YES, YOU MAY.

WHAT I LIKE ABOUT SUPERMAN IS THAT HE CAN *FLY!*

45

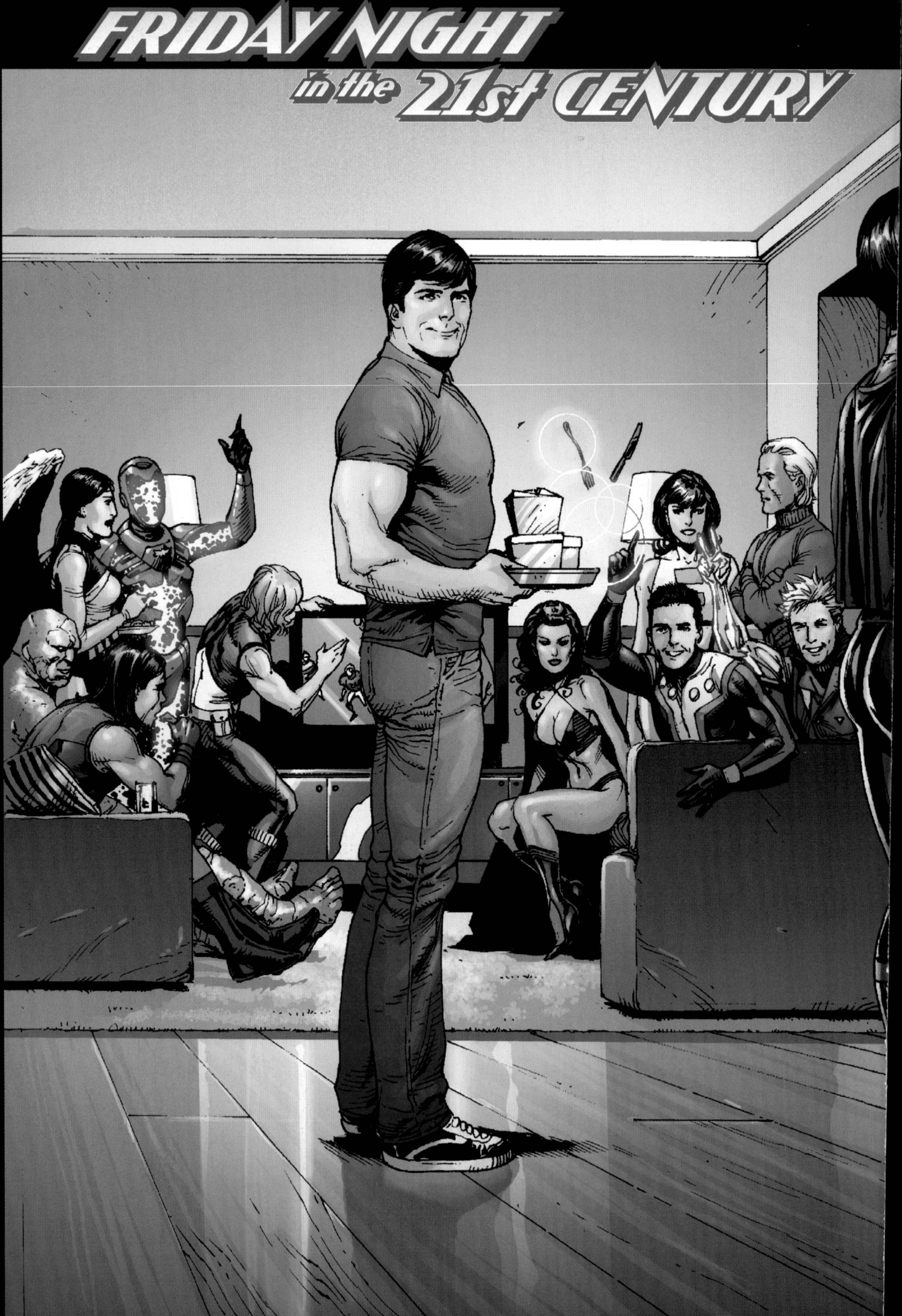
FRIDAY NIGHT
in the 21st CENTURY

GEOFF JOHNS & GARY FRANK: STORYTELLERS
BRAD ANDERSON: COLORIST   JOHN J. HILL: LETTERER
WIL MOSS: ASSOCIATE EDITOR   MATT IDELSON: EDITOR
SUPERMAN CREATED BY JERRY SIEGEL AND JOE SHUSTER

FLYING BOY
STOPPED FIRE!

TODAY THE PAPER RAN SOME MORE STORIES ABOUT ME.

Faulty electrical wiring was b for starting a fire in local farm Hubbard's ... what, or it the ... fire o been ... H claim ... fly flame breath, ... to a bizarre, ... cold front.

THE NEXT THING YOU KNOW HE'LL BE TELLING US *BIGFOOT* AND THE *LOCH NESS MONSTER* WERE THE ONES WHO DEFROSTED OUR CROPS LAST MONTH!

YOU ASK ME, IT WAS AN *ALIEN* FROM *OUTER SPACE.* HAHAHA--

DAD! LOOK OUT!

...CERTAINLY WON'T LOOK AT BEN HUBBARD THE SAME WAY AFTER EVERYTHING HE'S BEEN SAYING ABOUT THIS RIDICULOUS *"FLYING-BOY."*

TODAY MR. LANG SWERVED HIS CAR SO HE WOULDN'T HIT PETE'S GOLDEN RETRIEVER.

EEERRRRR

HNNNGHH!

TODAY I GOT SO CLOSE TO LANA LANG I COULD SMELL HER PERFUME.

BUT LAST WEEK WAS STILL **BETTER.**

LAST WEEK I WASN'T ALONE.

IT HAPPENED ON A MONDAY.

HEY, CLARK! WE'RE ALL HEADING TO FRITTER'S FIELD FOR A GAME OF BASEBALL. YOU WANNA COME?

PA ALWAYS WARNED ME ABOUT PLAYING SPORTS WITH THE OTHER KIDS.

THE ONE TIME I DIDN'T LISTEN TO HIM, I BROKE PETE'S ARM IN THREE PLACES.

...UM, SORRY, PETE.

THEY SAID HE FELL ON IT WRONG, BUT I HEARD THE BONES SNAP WHEN HE RAN INTO ME.

I THINK MY ALLERGIES ARE ACTING UP AGAIN.

FRIDAY, YOU HAD A HEADACHE. TODAY, YOU GOT HAY FEVER. YOU'RE A REAL ALL-STAR, KENT.

C'MON, GUYS. I'LL BUY EVERYONE SODAS AFTER THE GAME.

SEE YOU TOMORROW, CLARK.

BYE, PETE.

EVERY DAY ALWAYS ENDED THE SAME...

BOOOOOM

...UNTIL MONDAY.

WHOA!

RANNK

UFFF!

INSIDE THE ROCKET THERE WAS A KID A LITTLE OLDER THAN ME. AT FIRST I THOUGHT HE MIGHT BE HURT OR WORSE FROM THE CRASH...

...BUT HE WAS OKAY.

THERE WASN'T EVEN A TEAR IN THE CLOTHES HE WORE. AND THEN HE DID SOMETHING I COULDN'T BELIEVE.

HE SPOKE KRYPTONESE.

HE SAID "SON OF JOR-EL!"

IS THIS... EARTH?

WAIT A SECOND. YOU SPEAK ENGLISH *TOO?!*

IF THIS IS *ENGLISH*...I GUESS I DO.

YOU SAID *"SON OF JOR-EL."* WHY?

...I KNOW THE NAME, BUT...BUT THAT'S ALL I CAN REMEMBER.

WHO IS JOR-EL?

58

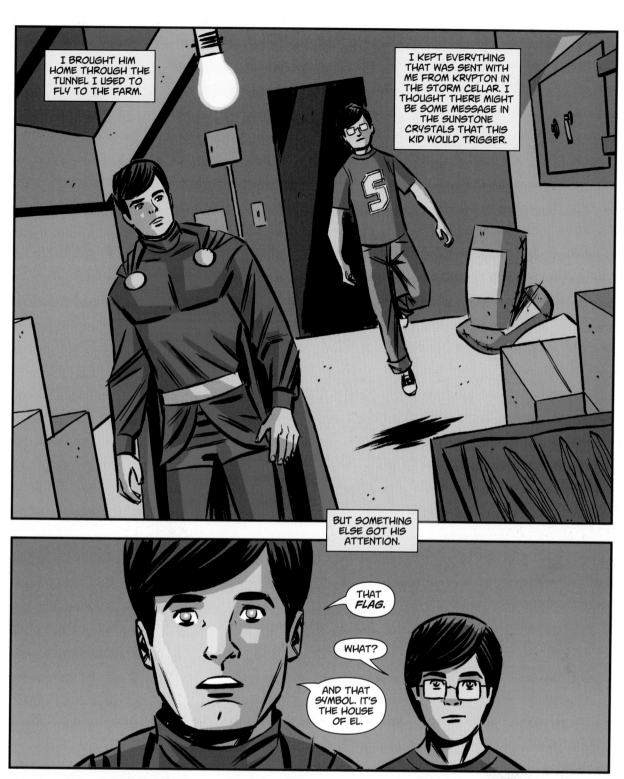

I BROUGHT HIM HOME THROUGH THE TUNNEL I USED TO FLY TO THE FARM.

I KEPT EVERYTHING THAT WAS SENT WITH ME FROM KRYPTON IN THE STORM CELLAR. I THOUGHT THERE MIGHT BE SOME MESSAGE IN THE SUNSTONE CRYSTALS THAT THIS KID WOULD TRIGGER.

BUT SOMETHING ELSE GOT HIS ATTENTION.

THAT *FLAG*.

WHAT?

AND THAT SYMBOL. IT'S THE HOUSE OF EL.

I THINK THAT'S WHERE I CAME FROM.

ALL THE EVIDENCE WAS THERE, WASN'T IT? I WASN'T THE ONLY ONE THAT ESCAPED KRYPTON.

I DIDN'T WANT TO BE ALONE.

AND NOW I WASN'T.

THANK YOU SO MUCH, MRS. KENT. WHAT'S THIS CALLED?

HAM AND CHEESE, DEAR.

IT LOOKS VERY GOOD.

HOW CAN YOU BE SO *SURE* OF THIS, SON?

HE SPOKE MY LANGUAGE, PA. HE HAS POWERS LIKE I DO.

HE *FELL* OUT OF THE *SKY* IN A ROCKET--

THAT LOOKED *NOTHING* LIKE *YOURS.*

I UNDERSTAND WHY YOU WANT TO BELIEVE HE'S KRYPTONIAN, BUT--

HE COULD BE *MORE* THAN JUST KRYPTONIAN, PA.

WITH EVERYTHING HE SAID ABOUT JOR-EL AND LANDING RIGHT HERE IN SMALLVILLE, I MEAN RIGHT IN *FRONT* OF ME...

...IT *HAS* TO BE MORE THAN COINCIDENCE.

MAYBE JOR-EL SENT *BOTH* OF HIS SONS TO EARTH.

PA SMILED AND NODDED AFTER THAT. I GUESS HE WANTED TO LET ME BELIEVE WHAT I WANTED TO BELIEVE.

YOU DON'T HAVE A NAME?

SO DID MA.

I'M AFRAID I DON'T REMEMBER IT, MA'AM.

HOW ABOUT *MON-EL* THEN?

JUST UNTIL I CAN REMEMBER MY *REAL* NAME.

WELL, OUR FAMILY NAME ALWAYS ENDED IN *"EL"*...IF YOU ARE, YOU KNOW...

Today
MON
15

WHAT DOES *MON* MEAN?

THAT'S TODAY. THAT'S *MONDAY.*

WE ALL DECIDED IT WOULD BE BEST TO KEEP MON-EL OUT OF SIGHT UNTIL I TAUGHT HIM HOW TO USE HIS POWERS. AND HOW TO HIDE THEM.

ON TUESDAY WE RESCUED A RIVERBOAT.

ON WEDNESDAY WE STOPPED A WRECK ON THE FREEWAY.

ON THURSDAY WE TOOK APART AN OUT-OF-CONTROL AMUSEMENT PARK RIDE.

BUT FRIDAY...

...FRIDAY WAS THE *BEST*. I FINALLY GOT TO PLAY BASEBALL.

STRIKE TWO!

HAHAHA!

AND NOBODY GOT HURT.

THE DAYS WERE REALLY GREAT.

BUT THE NIGHTS WERE A DIFFERENT STORY.

MON-EL? ARE YOU ALL RIGHT?

YOU WERE SPEAKING THAT WEIRD LANGUAGE AGAIN.

I'M SORRY I WOKE YOU, KAL. THE DREAMS ARE GETTING STRONGER.

I SEE AN EXPLOSION AND THEN HEAR A VOICE. IT SOUNDS LIKE MY VOICE. IT KEEPS SHOUTING...

"...YOU DON'T BELONG HERE."

I KNEW EXACTLY HOW HE FELT.

YOU DON'T HAVE TO DO THIS.

I NEED TO MAKE SURE I AM WHO WE THINK I AM.

YOU SAID YOU HAD A *KRYPTONITE* ROCK.

IN THAT SAFE, BUT--

IF YOU EXPOSE ME TO IT, WE'LL KNOW I'M KRYPTONIAN.

KRYPTONITE IS *POISONOUS* TO YOU AND ME. IT COULD HURT--

AND IF IT *DOES*, MAYBE I'LL BE ABLE TO SLEEP TONIGHT.

PLEASE, KAL.

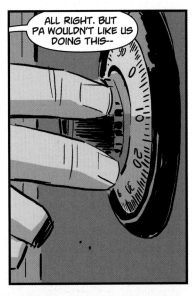

ALL RIGHT. BUT PA WOULDN'T LIKE US DOING THIS--

MON-EL?

AAAHHH!

HE GOT SICK AND BUCKLED OVER IN PAIN. HIS SKIN TURNED WHITE.

BUT IT WAS IMPOSSIBLE. I HADN'T EVEN *OPENED* THE BOX YET. THE KRYPTONITE WAS STILL ENCASED IN *LEAD*.

I REMEMBER, KAL. I REMEMBER...

...MY NAME IS *LAR GAND*.

"I AM FROM THE PLANET *DAXAM*.

"SECOND IN ORBIT AROUND THE SUN *VALOR*.

"I WAS A SEEKER THERE, STUDYING FORBIDDEN LORE.

"DURING MY RESEARCH, I FOUND DEVICES THAT HAD RECORDED DATA FROM THE FAR-OFF PLANET OF KRYPTON THE DAY IT EXPLODED.

"IT ALSO PRESERVED A MESSAGE FROM A ROCKET FIRED INTO SPACE SECONDS BEFORE KRYPTON'S DESTRUCTION.

"THE ONLY WORDS THEY COULD MAKE OUT WERE 'SON OF JOR-EL.'

"NO ONE KNEW WHAT WAS IN THE ROCKET OR WHERE IT WENT. SO I TOOK IT UPON MYSELF TO TRY TO *FIND* IT.

"I TRACKED ITS PATH TO A PLACE DEVOID OF ALL EXTRA-TERRESTRIAL AWARENESS.

"*EARTH*.

"MY COMPATRIOTS WARNED ME OF THE DANGERS BEYOND DAXAM, BUT I WAS DESPERATE TO SEE IF ANY RELICS FROM KRYPTON HAD SURVIVED.

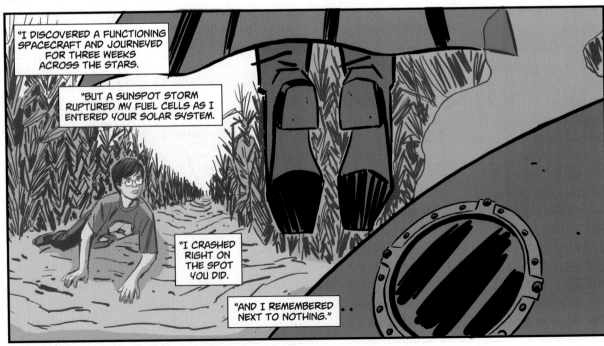

"I DISCOVERED A FUNCTIONING SPACECRAFT AND JOURNEYED FOR THREE WEEKS ACROSS THE STARS.

"BUT A SUNSPOT STORM RUPTURED MY FUEL CELLS AS I ENTERED YOUR SOLAR SYSTEM.

"I CRASHED RIGHT ON THE SPOT YOU DID.

"AND I REMEMBERED NEXT TO NOTHING."

MON-EL LOOKED UP AT THE PHANTOM ZONE PROJECTOR.

THE PHANTOM ZONE PROJECTOR?

...PUT ME IN IT...

PUT YOU *IN* IT? I CAN'T!

IT'S A DIMENSION FULL OF *NOTHING* BUT THE KRYPTONIAN CRIMINALS SENTENCED TO IT.

...IT'S A PLACE WHERE TIME STANDS STILL...

...IT'S THE *ONLY* WAY, KAL.

I DON'T EVEN KNOW HOW TO GET YOU *OUT.* THAT LEAD BOX. THAT STUPID LEAD *BOX!*

I SHOULD'VE NEVER...

...I'M SO SORRY.

MON-EL SMILED BUT HE DIDN'T SAY ANYTHING ELSE. HE COULDN'T.

AS HE FADED FROM SIGHT, I TOLD HIM I'D FIND A *CURE* ONE DAY.

FWASH

EVEN IF IT TOOK A THOUSAND YEARS.

MA SAID IT'S BETTER TO HAVE SPENT SOME TIME WITH SOMEONE LIKE ME THAN TO NEVER HAVE AT ALL.

I WISH IT WAS MONDAY AGAIN.

End.

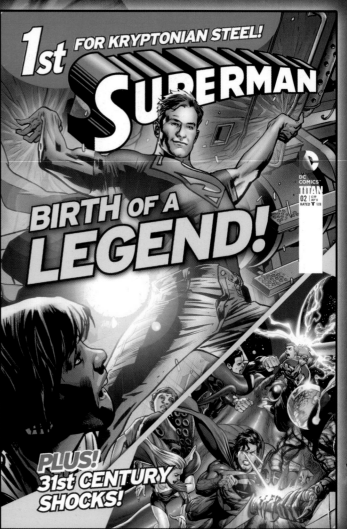

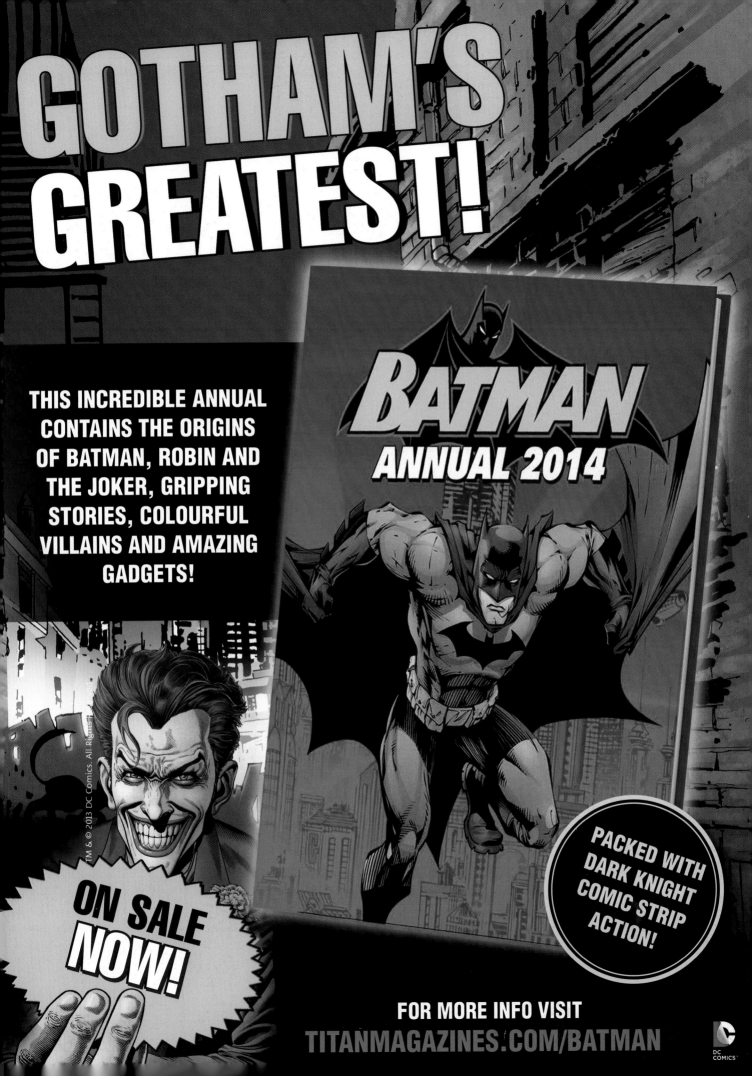